Gravitational Lens Illusions

David Michalets

December 6, 2021

Table of Contents

Introduction

This book is about mechanisms for bending the path of light. The important 1919 Eddington Experiment is reviewed. This book will reference many galaxies and galaxy clusters. Rather than bringing color images into this black and white book, a reference web page provides links to original source files with their high-resolution images.

Both the right and wrong mechanisms are explained. The title implies there are observations associating an illusion with a gravitational lens. A gravitational lens is based on a simple assumption, that either the force of gravity or curvature of space-time can bend the path of light,

The requirements or conditions for this assumption must be clearly defined. This book describes several scenarios with specific requirements. Given the same scenario, another mechanism is described that explains how the path of light can be bent, but not by gravity or space-time. If the requirements for a gravitational lens are not met, then the gravitational lens conjecture must be discarded, and an alternate mechanism is provided based on the specific conditions of the observation.

This is the scenario when the observed behavior is real, but unexpected. Therefore, a gravitational lens is invoked incorrectly to claim the lens caused the observation. By invoking a lens, the observation must be an illusion, not real.

A gravitational lens is the simple excuse when an observed behavior in distant galaxy clusters cannot be explained.

Examples of this excuse include:

1) A ring-like feature is incorrectly dismissed as an Einstein Ring,
2) Arcs or a ring around a distant galaxy,

3) A high redshift object is in the vicinity of lower redshift objects.

For (2), each arc or ring, claimed to be an illusion, is explained because each is a real observed behavior. The key realization is each is a plasma phenomenon.

This book begins with describing the behaviors of light and plasma. This background is the foundation of the explanation of the true nature of the arcs and rings identified in (2); some are found near only the giant elliptical galaxies in distant clusters having many galaxies.

There are several rings around objects in our solar system. These objects include several planets and even an asteroid. The planet Saturn has a series of bright, real rings; the other gas giants have faint circular rings. Everyone agrees these rings in our solar system are real because the rings contain particles which reflect sunlight. Unfortunately, astronomers are inconsistent when never accepting rings being found beyond our solar system. This is because cosmology has not integrated plasma physics.

The planet Jupiter is known to have a circular ring of non-luminous plasma, sometimes called a torus, in its magnetosphere.
A circular ring or arc (a segment of a circle) around a distant galaxy is consistently declared an illusion caused by a theoretical gravitational lens, despite the acceptance of the real rings within our solar system and a few notable rings on the scale of galaxies. One should expect a rational and justified explanation for unusual celestial objects, instead of an excuse of an illusion. Even if the mechanism is not fully understood, an illusion is not an acceptable explanation; cosmologists must learn plasma physics uncertainty

explained. The misleading 1919 solar eclipse experiment by Eddington set the pivotal precedent for an illusion to be acceptable in cosmology. This mistake resulted in the acceptance of more illusions having no basis in classical physics, like dark matter and dark energy. These conjectures remain undetected simply because they do not exist. Illusions are not solutions.

All can see these celestial rings in distant galaxy clusters, but cosmologists claim the rings are not real. This claim of an illusion must have evidence (like done for mirages in the desert), or the unjustified claim of illusion should be unacceptable, especially when a suitable explanation is available after considering plasma physics. When cosmologists ignore electromagnetism, the result is usually a mistake. One prominent example of this mistake is dark matter which is the excuse when the M31 magnetic field was ignored. A magnetic field drives the disk rotation, not gravity as incorrectly assumed.

In every case of a distant celestial arc being an illusion caused by a lens, there is never proper evidence for the scenario's combination (like an object's type, its magnitude, mass, size, and distance for the respective participants: 1) real light source, and 2) the lens object, whose mass is causing distant light to bend creating the claimed illusion. If the exact angles and distribution of proposed dark matter are not explicitly defined, then it is an incomplete solution and so without all the details for verification, it is an unacceptable solution.

Several real rings are described. The well-known illusions from a gravitational lens are described, including the Einstein Ring. I tried to find as many as possible. There is no published list, so there are probably more. The likely mechanism for the real ring, to replace the illusion by a lens, is explained for each.

The Saturn rings have been the subject of many studies, but their formation mechanism might never be conclusive because the formation of the planetary rings was never observed by astronomers.

Rings on the scale of galaxies could be difficult to demonstrate on the scale of Earth-bound experiments. Therefore, thorough experiments using distant giant elliptical galaxies are currently not practical on Earth.

This is a summary of the 15 sections:

Introduction describes the goal of this document and a summary of its sections.

1)   Light section describes various aspects and behaviors of light

2)   Plasma section describes various aspects of plasma, especially the tendency to form filaments. This section is a compressed course in some of plasma physics, where terms arise to subsequent sections.

3)   Jupiter section describes the circular plasma ring in its magnetosphere.

4)   Gravitational Lens section describes this theoretical behavior which is claimed to drive the illusion of distant celestial rings.

5)   Eddington Experiment section describes the pivotal experiment which is the basis of claiming the lens effect by gravity on light is real.

6)   Dr. Edward Dowdye is a scientist who measured and explained how star light can be bent when passing through the solar corona. His work proved that gravity or space-time curvature are not the correct mechanism for the observations of the Eddington Experiment in 1919.

7)   Ring Galaxies section describes several ring galaxies, which are accepted as real rings of stars, not illusions. This galaxy type has specific requirements; these simple rules distinguish between an Einstein Ring and a Ring Galaxy.

8)   Section of Galaxies with External Arcs describes several claimed illusions, using excerpts from the original sources.

9)   Arc Mechanism section explains the correct mechanism for these external arcs, which are found near bright galaxies in very distant clusters, and which are claimed to be illusions by a lens.

10) Microlensing explains the claimed illusion with magnified distant objects,

11) High Redshift Objects section identifies applications of a lens as an illusion for high redshift objects in galaxy clusters.

12) Particle Rings describes known circular particle rings around bodies in our solar system.

13) Black Hole section explains this object which is claimed to have a force of gravity too strong, or space-time curvature too steep, for light to escape.

14) Final Conclusion summarizes the points in the book.

15) References section describes how to access the external, internet references on each page.

For example, when a paragraph on page 9 has an on-line reference, then [R9] is shown after that paragraph. The References web page will have this page number and the link to this web reference. This technique enables the reader to check the entire original source using the references web page for this book, but only when the source is of interest. Perhaps during the first read-through, the interruption is avoided.

Some internet references include both text and accompanying images.

Most of the galaxies and clusters referenced in sections 7 and 8 have 2 links within this external web page: 1) its web article(s) having its description; 2) its image.

By clicking on the link to an image, the full color image can be quickly viewed, scrolled, and zoomed, as needed.

This format enables the reader to review only the images without having to find them within long articles. The page of references for an analysis of arcs and rings on the galactic scale has many sources via links, often more than one link per page in this document.

The page numbers in the reference web page are manual entries. Every entry was checked, but please accept a deviation of a page number. The topic on the page is provided to match the link.

1 Light

The mechanism for the propagation of light was explained by James Clerk Maxwell followed by contributions by others (noted below) around that time.

Einstein wrongly assumed mass had a velocity limit at c, the velocity of light in a vacuum.

There are various claims of a speed limit for light and for mass.

A helpful YouTube video is titled: [R10]
Why is the speed of light what it is? Maxwell equations visualized

This video clearly explains Maxwell's mechanism of propagating electric and magnetic fields, and its velocity limit set by the medium, but unfortunately concludes with a drastic mistake when mentioning Einstein.

Brief description of Maxwell's equations:

Maxwell's equations explain how these [light] waves can physically propagate through space. The changing magnetic field creates a changing electric field through Faraday's law. In turn, that electric field creates a changing magnetic field through Maxwell's addition to Ampère's law. This perpetual cycle allows these waves, now known as electromagnetic radiation, to move through space at velocity c. [R10]

Observation:

Relative permittivity is the factor by which the electric field between the charges is decreased relative to vacuum.

Observation:

There is also a factor for magnetic susceptibility.

The propagation of light is a self-propagating series of electric and magnetic fields. Its velocity is determined **only** by the medium. An instantaneous change in medium causes an instantaneous change in propagation velocity. This transition is observed with the illusion of a break in a line at the surface of water.

This propagation begins and continues at the same velocity regardless of any velocity of the source of its propagation.

Einstein had nothing to do with the constant velocity of light, though that is one of his postulates.
Maxwell thoroughly explained the basis of this limit.

Some question whether a moving light source affects the velocity of its light. Einstein had thought experiments about that, but he stated in his Second Postulate of Special Relativity that its velocity is constant.
The velocity of light propagation is always defined by the medium.

The velocity and direction of a light source affects the distribution of energy in the light but not its rate of propagation.

While the light source is moving, it has kinetic energy.

In thermodynamics, energy cannot be lost or gained but only exchanged or transformed.

Around the sphere of radiated energy, wavelengths are reduced in the direction of travel or increased in the opposite direction. Each wavelength change is determined by the velocity and direction at that point relative to c, which is the constant velocity of light in a vacuum. If the light source is in a medium, the z is the same because the medium affects the propagation not the initiation. Total energy is maintained around the radiated sphere at the instant of emission, but its distribution can change by the Doppler effect and the propagation velocity of the light emission cannot be affected.

The velocity and direction of a moving light source has no effect on the velocity of its light.

Einstein had a claim for a limit on the velocity of mass, which is a mistake.

He worked only with the context of a moving observer, the "special" observer in both "general" and "special" relativity.

Einstein's belief, of a velocity limit on mass, was shared by others in the 1800's, but has no justification in physics.

For many years, Einstein's unjustified belief of a speed limit on mass has been refuted.

Superluminal jets have been observed.

In 1993, Thomson et al. suggested that the (outer) jet of the quasar 3C 273 is nearly collinear to our line-of-sight. Superluminal motion of up to ~9.6c has been observed along the (inner) jet of this quasar.

Superluminal motion of up to 6c has been observed in the inner parts of the jet of M87. To explain this in terms of the "narrow-angle" model, the jet must be no more than 19° from our line-of-sight. [R13]

Observation:

The Doppler Effect and a redshift > 1 are explained in several of my books. That behavior is not relevant to rings around galaxies, but a thorough explanation of light is available if this section is inadequate.

A plasmoid, like in 3C 273 or M87, holds substantial electromagnetic energy. The sustained force of a magnetic field on charged particles can result in velocities far faster than c and this has been measured many times.

The motion of mass is a process independent of the medium except for friction from a surface. Space beyond an atmosphere provides no friction.

Friction is an exchange of kinetic energy of the moving body to thermal energy in the surface. Friction does not define a velocity limit.

Applying a force to a mass results in its acceleration, when not rigidly bound. The force can be maintained for a specific time of acceleration to achieve the desired velocity. This is a continuous transfer of energy from the source to the body's kinetic energy.

This process of energy transfer is observed during every launch of a space probe. Power is the amount of force during a time. The force required is determined by the mass and the time required for the desired velocity.

The available power is determined by the fuel supply, which is "full" at the moment of launch. The number and design of the respective stages determines the final velocity of the final stage which has the lowest mass, where individual stages provide the required amount of power for the velocity of the remaining stages. Increasing the initial power can increase the final velocity.

Once a mass is in motion it has kinetic energy. It must maintain that energy, so it remains in motion, until this energy is transferred, like with friction. Friction is a transfer of kinetic energy into thermal energy.

While a force continues to transfer more energy into kinetic energy of a body, the velocity must increase. There is no velocity limit from physics or thermodynamics during this energy transfer.

Einstein wrote equations causing changes to the moving observer when near the velocity of light, including relativistic mass, so their possible velocity limit was set in math, not in physics. At $c = v$, the relativistic mass is a mass divided by zero which is either infinite or not allowed!

Many authors writing about special relativity do not introduce relativistic mass.

Observation:

This unverified prediction by relativity is widely ignored. Some continue to claim all predictions by relativity were confirmed, but that is false.

It is critical to remember light always propagates at a velocity set by the medium at that instant. Some conjecture that the velocity of light is affected by the velocity of the light source. This is wrong. If it were true, then a red shift of $z>1$ for a Lyman-alpha emission line would be impossible to measure when light travels at a negative velocity. We measure that behavior with most quasars, to dismiss that conjecture.

Here is a definition of Prism:

Light changes speed as it moves from one medium to another (for example, from air into the glass of the prism). This speed change causes the light to be refracted and to enter the new medium at a different angle (Huygens principle). The degree of bending of the light's path depends on the angle that the incident beam of light makes with the surface, and on the ratio between the refractive indices of the two media (Snell's law). The refractive index of many materials (such as glass) varies with the wavelength or color of the light used, a phenomenon known as dispersion. This causes light of different colors to be refracted differently and to leave the prism at different angles, creating an effect similar to a rainbow. This can be used to separate a beam of white light into its constituent spectrum of colors. A similar separation happens with iridescent materials, such as a soap bubble.

Prisms will generally disperse light over a much larger frequency bandwidth than diffraction gratings, making them useful for broad-spectrum spectroscopy. Furthermore, prisms do not suffer from complications arising from overlapping spectral orders, which all gratings have. Prisms are sometimes used for the internal reflection at the surfaces rather than for dispersion. If light inside the prism hits one of the surfaces at a sufficiently steep angle, total internal reflection occurs and all of the light is reflected. This makes a prism a useful substitute for a mirror in some situations. [R16]

Observation:

A prism bends the path of light, because the prism is an inconsistent medium. Light cannot bend by any mechanism other than a change in the medium at that instant of its path.

2 Plasma

Plasma and its behaviors are very important in explaining the external rings.

Here is its definition:

Plasma is typically an electrically quasineutral medium of unbound positive and negative particles (i.e. the overall charge of a plasma is roughly zero). Although these particles are unbound, they are not "free" in the sense of not experiencing forces. Moving charged particles generate electric currents, and any movement of a charged plasma particle affects and is affected by the fields created by the other charges. In turn this governs collective behaviour with many degrees of variation. Striations or string-like structures, also known as Birkeland currents, are seen in many plasmas, like the plasma ball,
the aurora, lightning, electric arcs, solar
flares, and supernova remnants. They are sometimes associated with larger current densities, and the interaction with the magnetic field can form a magnetic
rope structure. High power microwave breakdown at atmospheric pressure also leads to the formation of filamentary structures. (See also Plasma pinch) [R18]

Observation:
Plasma is distinct from the other states of matter. In particular, describing a low-density plasma as merely an "ionized gas" is wrong and misleading, even though it is similar to the gas phase in that both assume no definite shape or volume.

Here is the definition of Birkelund currents.

Birkeland currents are also one of a class of plasma phenomena called a z-pinch, so named because the azimuthal magnetic fields produced by the current pinches the current into a filamentary cable. This can also twist, producing a helical pinch that spirals like a twisted or braided rope, and this most closely corresponds to a Birkeland current. Pairs of parallel Birkeland currents will also interact due to Ampère's force law: parallel Birkeland currents moving in the same direction will attract each other with an electromagnetic force inversely proportional to their distance apart whilst parallel Birkeland currents moving in opposite directions will repel each other. There is also a short-range circular component to the force between two Birkeland currents that is opposite to the longer-range parallel forces.

Electrons moving along a Birkeland current may be accelerated by a plasma double layer. If the resulting electrons approach the speed of light, they may subsequently produce a Bennett pinch, which in a magnetic field causes the electrons to spiral and emit synchrotron radiation that may include radio, visible light, x-rays, and gamma rays. [R18]

Here is a definition of double layer.

A double layer is a structure in a plasma consisting of two parallel layers of opposite electrical charge. The sheets of charge, which are not necessarily planar, produce localised excursions of electric potential, resulting in a relatively strong electric field between the layers and weaker but more extensive compensating fields outside, which restore the global potential. Ions and electrons within the double layer are accelerated, decelerated, or deflected by the electric field, depending on their direction of motion. [R19]

Here is a definition of a plasma pinch.

A pinch is the compression of an electrically conducting filament by magnetic forces, or a device that does such. The conductor is usually a plasma, but could also be a solid or liquid metal. [R19]

Observation:

Among the types of pinches noted in the Pinch topic:

Sheet pinch is an astrophysical effect, this arises from vast sheets of charge particles.

Z-pinch is where the current runs down the axis (or walls) of the cylinder while the magnetic field is azimuthal

Theta pinch is where the magnetic field runs down the axis of the cylinder, while the electric field is in the azimuthal direction (also called a thetatron)

Screw pinch is a combination of a Z-pinch and theta pinch (also called a stabilized Z-pinch, or θ-Z pinch).

Here is a description of a reversed field pinch.

This is an attempt to do a Z-pinch inside an endless loop. The plasma has an internal magnetic field. As you move out from the center of this ring, the magnetic field reverses direction. Also called a toroidal pinch.

Here is a definition of plasmoid.

A plasmoid is a coherent structure of plasma and magnetic fields. Plasmoids have been proposed to explain natural phenomena such as ball lightning, magnetic bubbles in the magnetosphere, and objects in cometary tails, in the solar wind, in the solar atmosphere, and in the heliospheric current sheet.

Plasmoids produced in the laboratory include field-reversed configurations, spheromaks, and in dense plasma focuses. The word plasmoid was coined in 1956 by Winston H. Bostick (1916-1991) to mean a "plasma-magnetic entity" The plasma is emitted not as an amorphous blob, but in the form of a torus. We shall take the liberty of calling this toroidal structure a plasmoid, a word which means plasma-magnetic entity. The word plasmoid will be employed as a generic term for all plasma-magnetic entities.

Plasmoids appear to be plasma cylinders elongated in the direction of the magnetic field. Plasmoids possess a measurable magnetic moment, a measurable translational speed, a transverse electric field, and a measurable size. Plasmoids can interact with each other, seemingly by reflecting off one another. Their orbits can also be made to curve toward one another. [R21]

Here is a definition of Magnetohydrodynamics, MHD.

MHD or magneto-fluid dynamics or hydromagnetics) is the study of the magnetic properties and behaviour of electrically conducting fluids. Examples of such magneto-fluids include plasmas, liquid metals, salt water, and electrolytes. The word "magnetohydrodynamics" is derived from magneto- meaning magnetic field, hydro- meaning water, and dynamics meaning movement. The field of MHD was initiated by Hannes Alfvén, for which he received the Nobel Prize in Physics in 1970.

The fundamental concept behind MHD is that magnetic fields can induce currents in a moving conductive fluid, which in turn polarizes the fluid and reciprocally changes the magnetic field itself. The set of equations that describe MHD are a combination of the Navier–Stokes equations of fluid dynamics and Maxwell's equations of electromagnetism. These differential equations must be solved simultaneously, either analytically or numerically.

Electromagnetic or magnetic induction is the production of an electromotive force across an electrical conductor in a changing magnetic field.
Michael Faraday is generally credited with the discovery of induction in 1831, and James Clerk Maxwell mathematically described it as Faraday's law of induction. Lenz's law describes the direction of the induced field. Faraday's law was later generalized to become the Maxwell–Faraday equation, one of the four Maxwell equations in his theory of electromagnetism. [R22]

Here is a description of Electromagnetic induction.

Electromagnetic induction has found many applications, including electrical components such as inductors and transformers, and devices such as electric motors and generators. [R22]

Here is a description of discharge in gases.

Electric discharge in gases occurs when electric current flows through a gaseous medium due to ionization of the gas. Depending on several factors, the discharge may radiate visible light. The properties of electric discharges in gases are studied in connection with design of lighting sources and in the design of high voltage electrical equipment. [R23]

Here is a description of Townsend discharge.

The Townsend discharge or Townsend avalanche is a gas ionisation process where free electrons are accelerated by an electric field, collide with gas molecules, and consequently free additional electrons. Those electrons are in turn accelerated and free additional electrons. The result is an avalanche multiplication that permits electrical conduction through the gas. The discharge requires a source of free electrons and a significant electric field; without both, the phenomenon does not occur.

Townsend put forward the hypothesis that positive ions also produce ion pairs, introducing a coefficient expressing the number of ion pairs generated per unit length by a positive ion (cation) moving from anode to cathode.

Townsend, Holst and Oosterhuis also put forward an alternative hypothesis, considering the augmented emission of electrons by the cathode caused by impact of positive ions. This introduced Townsend's second ionisation coefficient; the average number of electrons released from a surface by an incident positive ion, according to the following formula: [R23]

Observation:

The formula is not shown here; this book is not intended to replace an educational textbook having all the details; those details are not relevant to this book about lensing.

Filamentation also refers to the self-focusing of a high power laser pulse. At high powers, the nonlinear part of the index of refraction becomes important and causes a higher index of refraction in the center of the laser beam, where the laser is brighter than at the edges, causing a feedback that focuses the laser even more. The tighter focused laser has a higher peak brightness (irradiance) that forms a plasma. The plasma has an index of refraction lower than one, and causes a defocusing of the laser beam. The interplay of the focusing index of refraction, and the defocusing plasma makes the formation of a long filament of plasma that can be micrometers to kilometers in length. One interesting aspect of the filamentation generated plasma is the relatively low ion density due to defocusing effects of the ionized electrons.

Here is a description of Marklund Convection.

Marklund convection, named after Göran Marklund, is a convection process that takes place in filamentary currents of plasma. It occurs within a plasma with an associated electric field, that causes convection of ions and electrons inward towards a central twisting filamentary axis. A temperature gradient within the plasma will also cause chemical separation based on different ionization potentials.

In Marklund's paper, the plasma convects radially inwards towards the center of a cylindrical flux tube. During this convection, the different chemical constituents of the plasma, each having its specific ionization potential, enters into a progressively cooler region. The plasma constituents will recombine and become neutral, and thus no longer under the influence of the electromagnetic forcing. The ionization potentials will thus determine where the different chemicals will be deposited.

This provides an efficient means to accumulate matter within a plasma. In a partially ionized plasma, electromagnetic forces act on the non-ionized material indirectly through the viscosity between the ionized and non-ionized material.

Hannes Alfvén showed that elements with the lowest ionization potential are brought closest to the axis, and form concentric hollow cylinders whose radii increase with ionization potential. The drift of ionized matter from the surroundings into the rope means that the rope acts as an ion pump, which evacuates surrounding regions, producing areas of extremely low density. [R25]

There are 8 goals for the above excerpts:

1) Background on plasma filaments,

2) Birkelund currents and the Z-pinch,

3) Double Layer,

4) Electric discharges in the filament can be visible,

5) Toroidal pinch is relevant to the known toroid around Jupiter,

6) Plasmoids, which are toroids, can be ejected from a Z-pinch and can sometimes become a quasar when the ejection is from the Z-pinch within a Seyfert spiral galaxy whose core provides the metallic ions accompanying the ejected plasmoid to become a quasar,

7) Townsend effect is driven by positive ions impacting on the plasma filament. This effect is relevant to the observed luminous arcs and circles found only in distant clusters of large galaxies. M31 or Andromeda Galaxy is known to emit positive ions. The absorption lines of these ions cause the galaxy's measured blue shift, because we can measure the motion of these ions only in our line of sight.

I posted about M31 and its ions. [R26]

8) Marklund Convection explains the mixing of metallic ions into a plasma filament.

3 Jupiter

Jupiter has a known plasma ring in its magnetosphere. This ring involves interactions with ions emitted by the moon Io.

The magnetosphere of Jupiter is the cavity created in the solar wind by the planet's magnetic field. Extending up to seven million kilometers in the Sun's direction and almost to the orbit of Saturn in the opposite direction, Jupiter's magnetosphere is the largest and most powerful of any planetary magnetosphere in the Solar System, and by volume the largest known continuous structure.

Although overall the shape of Jupiter's magnetosphere resembles that of the Earth's, closer to the planet its structure is very different. Jupiter's volcanically active moon Io is a strong source of plasma in its own right, and loads Jupiter's magnetosphere with as much as 1,000 kg of new material every second. Strong volcanic eruptions on Io emit huge amounts of sulfur dioxide, a major part of which is dissociated into atoms and ionized by electron impacts and, to a lesser extent, solar ultraviolet radiation, producing ions of sulfur and oxygen. Further electron impacts produce higher charge state, resulting in a plasma of S+, O+, S2+, O2+ and S3+. They form the Io plasma torus: a thick and relatively cool ring of plasma encircling Jupiter, located near Io's orbit. The plasma temperature within the torus is 10–100 eV (100,000–1,000,000 K), which is much lower than that of the particles in the radiation belts—10 keV (100 million K). The plasma in the torus is forced into co-rotation with Jupiter, meaning both share the same period of rotation. The Io torus fundamentally alters the dynamics of the Jovian magnetosphere.
As a result of several processes—diffusion and interchange instability being the main escape mechanisms—the plasma slowly leaks away from Jupiter. As the plasma moves

further from the planet, the radial currents flowing within it gradually increase its velocity, maintaining co-rotation. These radial currents are also the source of the magnetic field's azimuthal component, which as a result bends back against the rotation. The particle number density of the plasma decreases from around 2,000 cm^{-3} in the Io torus to about 0.2 cm^{-3} at a distance of 35 RJ. In the middle magnetosphere, at distances greater than 10 RJ from Jupiter, co-rotation gradually breaks down and the plasma begins to rotate more slowly than the planet. Eventually at the distances greater than roughly 40 RJ (in the outer magnetosphere) this plasma is no longer confined by the magnetic field and leaves the magnetosphere through the magnetotail. As cold, dense plasma moves outward, it is replaced by hot, low-density plasma, with temperatures of up to 20 keV (200 million K) or higher) moving in from the outer magnetosphere. Some of this plasma, adiabatically heated as it approaches Jupiter, may form the radiation belts in Jupiter's inner magnetosphere.

While Earth's magnetic field is roughly teardrop-shaped, Jupiter's is flatter, more closely resembling a disk, and "wobbles" periodically about its axis. The main reasons for this disk-like configuration are the centrifugal force from the co-rotating plasma and thermal pressure of hot plasma, both of which act to stretch Jupiter's magnetic field lines, forming a flattened pancake-like structure, known as the magnetodisk, at the distances greater than 20 RJ from the planet. The magnetodisk has a thin current sheet at the middle plane, approximately near the magnetic equator. The magnetic field lines point away from Jupiter above the sheet and towards Jupiter below it. The load of plasma from Io greatly expands the size of the Jovian magnetosphere, because the magnetodisk creates an additional internal pressure which balances the pressure of the solar wind. In the absence of Io the distance from the planet to the magnetopause at the subsolar point would be no more than 42 RJ, whereas it is actually 75 RJ on average.

The configuration of the magnetodisk's field is maintained by the azimuthal ring current (not an analog of Earth's ring current), which flows with rotation through the equatorial plasma sheet. The Lorentz force resulting from the interaction of this current with the planetary magnetic field creates a centripetal force, which keeps the co-rotating plasma from escaping the planet. The total ring current in the equatorial current sheet is estimated at 90–160 million amperes. [R30]

Observation:

The interaction of the plasma ring with ions emitted by the Moon Io suggests a mechanism like the Townsend effect, but this Jovian torus is not luminous. Instead, the flow of ions to the ring maintains the torus.

Our observations of Jupiter's behaviors should apply to distant plasma behaviors, like celestial arcs or rings.

4 Gravitational Lens

Here is a description of the behavior.

A gravitational lens is a distribution of matter (such as a cluster of galaxies) between a distant light source and an observer, that is capable of bending the light from the source as the light travels towards the observer. This effect is known as gravitational lensing, and the amount of bending is one of the predictions of Albert Einstein's general theory of relativity. (Classical physics also predicts the bending of light, but only half of that predicted by general relativity.)
Although Einstein made unpublished calculations on the subject in 1912, Orest Khvolson (1924) and Frantisek Link (1936) are generally credited with being the first to discuss the effect in print. However, this effect is more commonly associated with Einstein, who published an article on the subject in 1936.

[From the image caption:]

What's large and blue and can wrap itself around an entire galaxy? A gravitational lens mirage. Pictured above, the gravity of a luminous red galaxy (LRG) has gravitationally distorted the light from a much more distant blue galaxy. More typically, such light bending results in two discernible images of the distant galaxy, but here the lens alignment is so precise that the background galaxy is distorted into a horseshoe -- a nearly complete ring. Since such a lensing effect was generally predicted in some detail by Albert Einstein over 70 years ago, rings like this are now known as Einstein Rings. Although LRG 3-757 was discovered in 2007 in data from the Sloan Digital Sky Survey (SDSS), the image shown above is a follow-up observation taken with the Hubble Space Telescope's Wide Field Camera 3. Strong gravitational lenses like LRG 3-757 are more than oddities --

their multiple properties allow astronomers to determine the mass and dark matter content of the foreground galaxy lenses. (citation is from APOD) [R33]

2 Observation:

1) There is a critical error in this description, about classical physics.

In Newton's time, no mass had been assigned to a photon simply because that term arose much later, after Einstein's 1905 paper. Maxwell lived many years after Newton, so Newton had no worthwhile definition of light available to him. A photon remains a mass-less quasi-particle, immune to gravity.

Maxwell worked with light only has a wave, as oscillating electric and magnetic fields, not particles moving within a medium. For Maxwell, light was never a particle. Neither of these scientists, both living many years before Einstein, would have predicted a specific angle of light bending by gravity when light had no assigned mass value. I can find no online reference detailing where this "prediction by classical physics" was made by whom and when. However. In the section Eddington Experiment, the work by Johann Georg von Soldner is referenced and the ambiguous origin of Einstein's prediction.

Isaac Newton was certainly interested in light, but his contributions do not match those of Maxwell. Newton was noted for his work with prisms and the colors in light.

In 1704, Newton published Opticks, in which he expounded his corpuscular theory of light.

He considered light to be made up of extremely subtle corpuscles, that ordinary matter was made of grosser corpuscles and speculated that through a kind of alchemical transmutation "Are not gross Bodies and Light convertible into one another, ... and may not Bodies receive much of their Activity from the Particles of Light which enter their Composition? [R34]

Observation:

Given Newton's speculation of light being convertible in its nature, I expect it unlikely or impossible for Newton to have assigned a precise mass to light for a precise prediction to be compared to Einstein's. Claiming Newton made such a precise prediction requires evidence, but there is none.

This attempted comparison of a prediction before to one later by Einstein is utterly baseless. This is a terrible attempt to assign an unjustified credit to Einstein. Perhaps, this is because the 1919 prediction was not correctly tested, this claim is a diversion from that inadequacy.

2) The image and its caption reveal this object **cannot** be the result of a gravitational lens!

The complex ring has obvious structure. A lens can only bend the path of light and cannot change its color or appearance. The typical claimed arc by a lens is a very thin arc. It is wrong for a lensed object with either magnification or a varying structure along its length.

The hypothetical lens can only bend the path of light. The color of electromagnetic radiation is driven by the energy distribution within its continuum of wavelengths. To change its color, energy must be changed. Gravity alone has no energy to transfer to the passing light. Proposing just gravity can increase the energy in light passing at a distance violates the conservation of energy. The Doppler Effect uses the kinetic energy in the matter moving which can absorb or emit radiation. The object claimed to be a lens is not participating in any energy transfers with the passing light. The lens does not absorb or emit anything. All mass outside of the light path cannot affect the energy in the light.

The blue is not lensed because no galaxies possess that basic color; their spectrum is predominately synchrotron radiation which results in the color white from the mix in the continuum of wavelengths being emitted, though dust clouds can affect the appearance (darker or redder) depending on the line of sight and the viewing angle. Blue cannot result.

The most likely explanation for the color of blue is most likely from the Lyman-alpha emission line which is in ultraviolet; when the protons are moving away during the electron capture, then the wavelength redshifts toward a blue.
The topic's explanation of the colors within the complex ring violates thermodynamics.

The simple rule for a lensed object is it must have no structure. This object clearly violates that rule and cannot be a lensed object. Despite that conflict, this wrong example remains the selection for Wikipedia. Its use reveals there is no verification of articles and images matching the desired narrative for a lensed object according to the rules. The likely reason for its use is its image is striking. Most readers will not take the brief time to critique its features.

4.1 Light bending by curvature

Here is that explanation.

In general relativity, light follows the curvature of spacetime, hence when light passes around a massive object, it is bent. This means that the light from an object on the other side will be bent towards an observer's eye, just like an ordinary lens. In general relativity the speed of light depends on the gravitational potential (i.e. the metric) and this bending can be viewed as a consequence of the light traveling along a gradient in light speed. Light rays are the boundary between the future, the spacelike, and the past regions. The gravitational attraction can be viewed as the motion of undisturbed objects in a background curved geometry or alternatively as the response of objects to a force in a flat geometry. [R38]

Observation:

Spacetime is background independent. It is confined to the special, moving observer's reference frame. It is impossible for the moving observer to cause a "background curved geometry" as relativity is defined.

Light is the propagation of perpendicular, synchronized electric and magnetic fields. The velocity of this propagation is defined by the medium at that instant. It is impossible for this propagation to follow anyone's defined geometry.

A point source of electromagnetic radiation, or a spherical source like a star, generate a sphere of radiation, that propagates in all directions, so over time, the leading edge of this propagation is an expanding sphere of energy carried in the wavelength distribution from the source.

Light is not a particle but is a continuum of energy. The light emitted by a star is in the format of thermal radiation, having a continuum of wavelengths from ultraviolet to infrared. There is no quantized behavior in light. The photoelectric effect is a quantized behavior but the atom and its electron configuration drive the behavior, not light.

Spacetime is the incremental change in the special moving observer's motion, represented by dx, dy, dz, dct. Where "d" is delta for change in this value in Cartesian coordinates in the observer's reference frame. Curvature is implemented in theory by changing these values so the path of the moving observer can be changed, or curved, by changing these increments.

If the leading edge of the light's propagation were represented in an observer's reference frame by x,y,z, positions, it is impossible to change the path of its propagation by changing the coordinates of the leading edge of the propagation. This attempt to change the next increment of the path of propagation is impossible, given the definition of light by James Clerk Maxwell. Light continues its propagation until absorbed and its path cannot be changed by a 4-dimensional coordinate system. Coordinate systems enable a measurement. Nothing is driven by a coordinate system.

Spacetime cannot bend light.

5 Eddington Experiment

Description of the Eddington Experiment:

One of the first considerations of gravitational deflection of light was published in 1801, when Johann Georg von Soldner pointed out that Newtonian gravity predicts that starlight will be deflected when it passes near a massive object. Initially, in a paper published in 1911, Einstein had incorrectly calculated that the amount of light deflection was the same as the Newtonian value. There had been plans by an American team from the Lick Observatory to measure the amount of deflection by making observations of an eclipse in Brazil in 1912, but bad weather prevented observations being made. Eddington had taken part in a British expedition to Brazil to observe the 1912 eclipse but was interested in different measurements.

Although Einstein's main work on general relativity was not published until 1915, he was aware before then that his 1911 calculation had been wrong, and that in fact the predicted effect in the Newtonian model is only half the value predicted by general relativity. This suggested a possible test for his theory, and in 1913 Einstein asked George Ellery Hale to suggest a way of detecting the deflection of light from a star as it passed the Sun.

The eclipse was due to take place in the early afternoon of 29 May, at 2pm, but that morning there was a storm with heavy rain. Eddington wrote:

The rain stopped about noon and about 1.30 ... we began to get a glimpse of the sun. We had to carry out our photographs in faith. I did not see the eclipse, being too busy changing plates, except for one glance to make sure that it had begun and another half-way through to see how much cloud there was. We took sixteen photographs. They are all good of the sun, showing a very remarkable prominence; but the cloud has interfered with the star images. The last few photographs show a few images which I hope will give us what we need ...

Eddington developed the photographs on Principe, and attempted to measure the change in the stellar positions during the eclipse. On 3 June, despite the clouds that had reduced the quality of the plates, Eddington recorded in his notebook: "... one plate I measured gave a result agreeing with Einstein."

In the post-Newtonian tests of gravity, the parameterized post-Newtonian formalism parameterizes, in terms of ten adjustable parameters, all the possible departures from Newton's law of universal gravitation. The earliest parameterizations of the post-Newtonian approximation were performed by Eddington (1922). The parameter concerned with the amount of deflection of light by a gravitational source is the so-called Eddington parameter (γ). It is the best constrained of the ten post-Newtonian parameters.

The early accuracy of eclipse measurements, however, was poor. Dyson et al. quoted an optimistically low uncertainty in their measurement, which is argued by some to have been plagued by systematic error and possibly confirmation bias, although modern reanalysis of the dataset suggests that Eddington's analysis was accurate.

In 1801 Johann Georg von Soldner had pointed out that Newtonian gravity predicts that starlight will bend around a massive object, but the predicted effect is only half the value predicted by general relativity as calculated by Einstein in his 1911 paper. The results of Soldner were revived by the Nobel laureate Philipp Lenard in an attempt to discredit Einstein. Eddington had been aware in 1919 of the alternative predictions. Considerable uncertainty remained in these measurements for almost fifty years, until observations started being made at radio frequencies. It was not until the late 1960s that it was definitively shown that the amount of deflection was the full value predicted by general relativity, and not half that number.

The theory behind the experiment concerns the predicted deflection of light by the Sun. The first observation of light deflection was performed by noting the change in position of stars as they passed near the Sun on the celestial sphere. The approximate angular deflection $\delta\varphi$ for a massless particle coming in from infinity and going back out to infinity is given by the following formula: [the formula is not shown here due to the next statement.]

Although this formula is approximate, it is accurate for most measurements of gravitational lensing, due to the smallness of the ratio rs/b. For light grazing the surface of the sun, the approximate angular deflection is roughly 1.75 arcseconds. This is twice the value predicted by calculations using the Newtonian theory of gravity. It was this difference in the deflection between the two theories that Eddington's expedition and other later eclipse observers would attempt to observe.

Dyson, when planning the expedition in 1916, had chosen the 1919 eclipse because it would take place with the Sun in front of a bright group of stars called the Hyades. The brightness of these stars would make it easier to measure any changes in position. [R43]

Observation:

This description of the bad weather is important, but Eddington achieved his primary goal of seeking "a result agreeing with Einstein."

This experiment should have 2 goals:

1) Confirm Einstein's prediction,

2) Verify there is no conflicting evidence.

The second goal should have been just as important as the first.

The description of the observation mentions only the one star on the solar limb, which was the primary goal for the expedition. Unfortunately for this pivotal experiment, this particular selection offers 2 distinct mechanisms for its light to bend.

1) Hypothetical bending by gravity,

2) Known behavior of bending by atmospheric refraction.

At the solar limb, the solar atmosphere is at its maximum density by gravity pulling down loose plasma particles down to the photosphere surface. Their kinetic energy maintains an uneven distribution.

On the Earth: "you can actually see the Sun a few minutes before it rises and a few minutes after it sets" This is because of [atmospheric] refraction." Many have observed this behavior, when having a clear view of the horizon. [R44]

This refraction is why the second goal was so important. The constellation of Hyades provided stars to check. Using stars in Hyades was noted in 2016. The cloudy conditions imply only the Sun and only the bright star on its limb might be captured in any images.

With gravitational lensing, ALL objects in the view should have been affected, but by their distance from the Sun. I recall web articles from 2019 stating other observers, not Eddington, noted several stars and even a planet somewhat behind the Sun, were not shifted as expected' rough sky maps were included. Those old articles must have been purged from the web over time, and could not be found today, 2 years later.

When browsing for subsequent tests of stars not at the solar limb, no such tests are found. Apparently, these tests seek to repeat the original check of a prediction only at the limb.

Refraction occurs only at the limb. If that is the only star being checked, then refraction by the solar atmosphere has been confirmed numerous times.

Until all stars around the Sun are verified to match a prediction for each object's distance, this experiment cannot be considered thorough.

Gravitational lensing remains unconfirmed. The force of gravity does not interact with the propagation of electric and magnetic fields. Gravity is a force limited to only particles having mass.

The story about Einstein's prediction has a relevant reference in the story of Johann Georg von Soldner.

Soldner is now mostly remembered for having concluded — based on Newton's corpuscular theory of light — that light would be diverted by heavenly bodies. In a paper written in 1801 and published in 1804, he calculated the amount of deflection of a light ray by a star [...], one finds $\omega=0,84''$.

Albert Einstein calculated and published a value for the amount of gravitational light-bending in light skimming the Sun in 1911, leading Phillipp Lenard to accuse Einstein of plagiarising Soldner's result. [R45]

Observation:

So much emphasis has been made of comparing Einstein's prediction to that predicted by Newton's gravity.

When looking at the history of these two supposed predictions, it is unclear how valid either prediction is when comparing the origin and value of each.

6 Edward Dowdye

Edward Dowdye is a scientist who measured and explained how star light can be bent when passing through the solar corona. He demonstrates the angle is predictable based on where it enters the corona. This proves that gravity and space-time are not the correct mechanism for the observations of the Eddington Experiment in 1919.

He explained his work with the solar corona bending the light passing through it, in this YouTube video: [R47]

- Stars BEND LIGHT? General Relativity and Gravity with Dr. Edward Dowdye!

His web site has a page titled:

Why are the Einstein Rings not seen in the star-filled skies?

Gravitational light bending, as predicted by General Relativity, should be easily noticeable at multiple solar radii well into the empty vacuum space above the solar plasma rim.

Remarkably as it may seem, however, historically the solar light bending effect has been observed only at the solar rim, the refractive plasma atmosphere of the sun. This is strongly confirmed by a large number of very-long-baseline-interferometer (VLBI) measurements on the gravitational deflection of microwaves from radio pulsar sources that were deflected at the thin plasma rim of the sun at precisely the angle of 1.75 arcsec. [R47]

Observation:

This web page includes an animation of the observed angles of deflection. Deflection occurs only when the light path is through the corona. Relativity predicts a deflection which varies proportionally by distance from the solar limb. Therefore, relativity fails at all other observed paths, or not at the solar limb.

This page has this chart with Dowdye's test results:

Gravitational Deflection as function of Impact Parameter

(in units of the solar radius R)

Impact Parameter (solar radii R)	Observational History (arsec)	General Relativity (arcsec)
R	1.75	1.75
2R	< 0.875 to negligible	1/2 of 1.75
3R	negligible	1/3 of 1.75
nR	not observed	1/n of 1.75

Observation:

The only successful prediction by relativity is a star on the solar limb, with the maximum refraction in the solar atmosphere. Off the limb, the predictions fail.

7 Ring Galaxies

Each galaxy has its section number as 7.x All have links in section References to web articles and images.

7.1 Hoag's Object

Its description:

Hoag's Object is a non-typical galaxy of the type known as a ring galaxy. The galaxy is named after Arthur Hoag who discovered it in 1950 and identified it as either a planetary nebula or a peculiar galaxy with eight billion stars, spanning roughly 100,000 light years.

A nearly perfect ring of young hot blue stars circles the older yellow nucleus of this ring galaxy c. 600 million light-years away in the constellation Serpens. The diameter of the 6 arcsecond inner core of the galaxy is about 17±0.7 kly (5.3±0.2 kpc) while the surrounding ring has an inner 28″ diameter of 75±3 kly (24.8±1.1 kpc) and an outer 45″ diameter of 121±4 kly (39.9±1.7 kpc). The galaxy is estimated to have a mass of 700 billion suns. By way of comparison, the Milky Way galaxy has an estimated diameter of 150-200 kly and consists of between 100 and 500 billion stars and a mass of around 1.54 trillion suns. The gap separating the two stellar populations may contain some star clusters that are almost too faint to see. Though ring galaxies are rare, another more distant ring galaxy (SDSS J151713.93+213516.8) can be seen through Hoag's Object, between the nucleus and the outer ring of the galaxy, at roughly the one o'clock position in the image shown here.
Noah Brosch and colleagues showed that the luminous ring lies at the inner edge of a much larger neutral hydrogen ring.

In the initial announcement of his discovery, Hoag proposed the hypothesis that the visible ring was a product of gravitational lensing. This idea was later discarded because the nucleus and the ring have the same redshift, and because more advanced telescopes revealed the knotty structure of the ring, something that would not be visible if the ring were the product of gravitational lensing. [R52]

Observation:

This explicit distinction of knotty structure to discard lensing is not applied consistently, because other external rings also show knots and structure but are still claimed to be an illusion by a lens.

7.2 Cartwheel galaxy

Here is a description.

The Cartwheel Galaxy (also known as ESO 350-40 or PGC 2248) is a lenticular galaxy and ring galaxy about 500 million light-years away in the constellation Sculptor. It is an estimated 150,000 light-years diameter, and has a mass of about $2.9–4.8 \times 10^9$ solar masses; its outer ring has a circular velocity of 217 km/s.

It was discovered by Fritz Zwicky in 1941. Zwicky considered his discovery to be "one of the most complicated structures awaiting its explanation on the basis of stellar dynamics."

An estimation of the galaxy's span resulted in a conclusion of 150,000 light years, which is a moderate amount smaller than the Milky Way. [R53]

Observation:

This galaxy is still waiting for an explanation after 80 years. Perhaps, cosmology must learn to apply MHD.

7.3 RX J1131-1231

Here is its description.

RX J1131-1231 is a distant, supermassive-black-hole-containing quasar located about 6 billion light years from Earth in the constellation Crater.

In 2014, astronomers found that the X-rays being emitted are coming from a region inside the accretion disk located about three times the radius of the event horizon. This implies that the black hole must be spinning incredibly fast to allow the disk to survive at such a small radius. The measurement of the black hole's rotation is the first time astronomers have been able to directly measure the rotational speed of any black hole.

This determination was made by a team led by Rubens Reis of the University of Michigan using NASA's Chandra X-ray Observatory and the European Space Agency's XMM-Newton telescopes. The team observed the X-rays generated in the innermost regions of the disk circling and feeding the black hole that powers the quasar. By measuring the radius of the disk, the astronomers were able to calculate the black hole's rotational speed, which was almost half the speed of light. The rapid spin of the quasar indicates that the black hole is being fed by a vast supply of gas and dust.

However, the measurements would not have been possible without a rare alignment of the quasar and a giant elliptical galaxy (which is itself part of a cluster of other galaxies in line with the quasar) which lies between Earth and RX J1131-1231. This line-up provided a quadruple gravitational lens which magnified the light coming from the quasar. The strong gravitational lensing effect associated with RX J1131-1231 has also produced measured time delays; that is, in one image the lensed quaser [sic] will be observed before the other image. [R54]

Observation:

There is no evidence that an accretion disk, having a completely unknown composition (elements, density, etc.), can remain intact as condensed matter to emit thermal radiation having X-ray energy. Thermal usually spans from ultraviolet to infrared, never with X-ray. X-ray devices for medical applications employ a mechanism for synchrotron, never thermal. An accretion disk is pure conjecture.

This outer ring is emitting synchrotron radiation, which often spans from X-ray to infrared or even radio.

The black hole in the story is nonsense.

The AGN in every quasar is a plasmoid, like the one recently imaged in M87 elliptical galaxy using radio wavelengths. Wal Thornhill provided a good explanation of a plasmoid in a YouTube video: Thornhill: Black Hole or Plasmoid? [R55]

There is no evidence of a "quadruple gravitational lens."

Gravity cannot increase the intensity or energy of the light wavelengths passing by! And by 4x!

This is an undefined energy transfer with no identified source of the external energy.

Apparently, Cosmologists just violate accepted physics when no other explanation can be found. They refuse to recognize the known sources of synchrotron radiation which can attain X-ray energies.

7.4 AM 0644-741

Here is its description:

AM 0644-741, also known as the Lindsay-Shapley Ring, is an unbarred lenticular galaxy, and a ring galaxy, which is 300 million light-years away in the southern constellation Volans.

The yellowish nucleus was once the center of a normal spiral galaxy, and the ring which currently surrounds the center is 150,000 light years in diameter. The ring is theorized to have formed by a collision with another galaxy, which triggered a gravitational disruption that caused dust in the galaxy to condense and form stars, which forced it to then expand away from the galaxy and create a ring.

The ring is a region of rampant star formation dominated by young, massive, hot blue stars. The pink regions along the ring are rarefied clouds of glowing hydrogen gas that is fluorescing as it is bombarded with strong ultraviolet light from the blue stars. [R57]

Observation:

The "glowing hydrogen gas" is area of protons capturing electrons and emitting the Lyman-alpha line in UV, as the fresh neutral atoms form.

7.5 SPD.81

From "Gravity lens reveals dwarf dark galaxy"

[caption:]
Composite image of the gravitational lens SDP.81. The lensing object – a large quantity of mass between us and a more distant galaxy – is shown here as the blue center object (Hubble optical image). The more distant galaxy is shown in the red arcs (acquired by the ALMA telescope). The white dot near left lower arc segment shows the possible location of a dark dwarf galaxy. Image via Y. Hezaveh, Stanford Univ.; ALMA (NRAO/ESO/NAOJ); NASA/ESA Hubble Space Telescope.

A fascinating area of research in astronomy nowadays is the search for dwarf galaxies containing large amounts of dark matter. A superabundance of dwarf dark galaxies is thought to exist in our universe. They're thought to be much like our Milky Way's known satellite galaxies in that they orbit a larger galaxy, but different because they contain substantial amounts of unseen matter, the mysterious dark matter believed to make up much of the mass of our universe. To have so much mass in an unknown form of course tantalizes astronomers. Late last week (April 14, 2016), scientists with the ALMA telescope array in Chile announced their conclusion that they've found a dwarf dark galaxy via a gravitational lens. They're excited because it might mean a new way of studying dark matter in the distant universe, and because it might reveal the presence of more dwarf dark galaxies, which astronomers hope – for the sake of their current theories about the universe – do exist.
A detailed analysis of the image above of the gravitational lens SDP.81 – located some 4 billion light-years away – indicated the little dark galaxy's presence. The astronomers said in their statement that:

... this discovery paves the way for ALMA to find many more such objects and could help astronomers address important questions on the nature of dark matter.
And it could help them answer questions about dwarf dark galaxies, which have so far proven difficult to find.

One of these experimental images was that of an Einstein ring, which was produced by the gravity of a massive foreground galaxy bending the light emitted by another galaxy nearly 12 billion light-years away. [R59]

Observation:

The center galaxy must have a magnetic field causing the Lorentz tangential force to push protons in their circular path.

The red arc is probably the loose protons capturing electrons and emitting the Balmer-alpha line having its red wavelength, as the fresh neutral atoms form.

The term "experimental images" implies this image is computer-generated, not as observed.

There is no dark matter.

8 Galaxies With External Arcs

Each galaxy or cluster has its section number as 8.x. All have links in section of References. Their order is not significant. Perhaps there are more, but I found only these.

8.1 Abell 370

Here is its description:

Abell 370 is a galaxy cluster located approximately 4 billion light-years away from the Earth (at redshift z = 0.375), in the constellation Cetus. Its core is made up of several hundred galaxies. It was catalogued by George Abell, and is the most distant of the clusters he catalogued.
In the 1980s astronomers of Toulouse Observatory discovered a gravitational lens in space between Earth and Abell 370. A curious arc had been observed earlier near the cluster, but the astronomers were able to recognize it as this phenomenon. [R61]

Observation:

There is a bright filament to the right of a giant elliptical galaxy. This filament is not an arc, which would have a constant radius as part of a circle. This filament has structure at its bottom end. That discards the lens mechanism. The filament appears slightly red. The Balmer-alpha emission line is at 6563 A, or the color red. That emission line comes from a proton capturing an electron at a lower kinetic energy, than the Lyman-alpha line, which is in ultraviolet.

This "curious arc" cannot be from a lens when having structure.

8.2 Abell 383

Here is its description:

Abell 383 is a galaxy cluster in the Abell catalogue.
[From the image caption:]

The giant cluster of elliptical galaxies in the centre of this image contains so much dark matter mass that its gravity bends light. This means that for very distant galaxies in the background, the cluster's gravitational field acts as a sort of magnifying glass, bending and concentrating the distant object's light towards Hubble. [R62]

Observation:

There is a bright filament to the lower right of a giant elliptical galaxy. This filament is not an arc, which would have a constant radius as part of a circle. This filament has varying intensity along its length. That inconsistency should discard the lens mechanism.

Apparently, dark matter must be invoked to explain this "concentration" of light in the filament, so the fictitious lens can remain as its explanation.

Plasma filaments nearly always get fictitious dark matter because cosmologists ignore plasma physics.

8.3 Abell 1413

Here is its description:

Abell 1413 is located 2 billion light years away from Earth between the constellations of Leo and Coma Berenices. It is one of 4,073 clusters of galaxies at redshift (meaning they are moving away from earth,) that are somewhat close to the Earth. Abell 1413 holds about 300 galaxies together with its strong gravity. Due to the strong interactions in the cluster, the material is heated up to 100 million degrees. Because of this intense heat, strong X-ray radiation is emitted from the cluster. [R63]

Observation:

When the intracluster medium is generating X-rays, the source must be synchrotron radiation, with electric currents (charges in motion) interacting with magnetic fields. X-rays cannot come from thermal radiation which requires condensed matter. This cluster's intracluster medium's "material" is not a liquid or solid. The stated extreme temperature has no justification.

The 300 galaxies are widely separated despite "strong gravity" in the cluster. This suggests the inverse-square-distance application of gravity's force is being violated for its supposed role. The force of electromagnetism is much stronger than gravity.

8.4 Abell 1689

Here is its description:

Abell 1689 is a galaxy cluster in the constellation Virgo nearly 2.2 billion light-years away. Abell 1689 is one of the biggest and most massive galaxy clusters known and acts as a gravitational lens, distorting the images of galaxies that lie behind it. It has the largest system of gravitational arcs ever found.
Abell 1689 shows over 160,000 globular clusters, the largest population ever found.
There is evidence of merging and gases in excess of 100 million degrees. The very large mass of this cluster makes it useful for the study of dark matter and gravitational lensing.
At the time of its discovery in 2008, one of the lensed galaxies, A1689-zD1, was the most distant galaxy found. [R64]

Observation:

One can only wonder how the total mass in this cluster could be calculated, given its diversity.

This cluster's "material" is not a liquid or solid. The stated extreme temperature has no justification. If it is calculated from assumptions for metallic emission lines then this is wrong. Ions capturing electrons moving in an electric field are not driven by this fictitious temperature.

There are many short, bright filaments scattered within this cluster. Some of the galaxies have unusual shapes, like a red one at upper right. The particular objects making up this "largest system of arcs" are not identified.

The bright blue filaments could be from Lyman-alpha emissions in ultraviolet. Red is from Balmer-alpha emissions.

A1689-zD1 has a claimed redshift of z=7.6, but the NASA/IPAC Extragalactic Database site has no spectra to justify this value. Every galaxy or quasar with z > 1 always get this wrong redshift from the shift of the Lyman-alpha emission line, when a high velocity proton captures a proton.

Every galaxy redshift comes from atoms in the line of sight from Earth. This z value does not arise from the galaxy. It certainly has nothing to do with the galaxy's velocity or distance.

There is no justification for the stated distance to this cluster.

There is no justification for the claim that A1689-zD1 was the most distant galaxy found.

Eventually, all bad data must be purged.

8.5 Abell 1835

Here is its description:

Abell 1835 is a galaxy cluster in the Abell catalogue. It is a cluster that also gravitational lenses more-distant background galaxies to make them visible to astronomers. The cluster has a red shift of around 75,900 km/s and spans 12'.
In 2004, one of the galaxies lensed by this cluster was proposed to be the most distant galaxy known, Galaxy Abell 1835 IR1916. [R66]

Observation:

Abell 1835 IR1916 is not in the NASA/IPAC Extragalactic Database site, when I looked. Every galaxy redshift comes from atoms in the line of sight from Earth. Its z value does not arise from the galaxy. It certainly has nothing to do with the galaxy's velocity or distance.

Since cosmology fails to recognize bad velocities, and will not disconnect redshift from velocity and distance, a gravitational lens is the excuse for the mistakes with the awkward, high redshift.

8.6 Abell 2218

Here is its description:

Abell 2218 is a cluster of galaxies about 2 billion light-years away in the constellation Draco. Acting as a powerful lens, it magnifies and distorts all galaxies lying behind the cluster core into long arcs. The lensed galaxies are all stretched along the cluster's center and some of them are multiply imaged. Those multiple images usually appear as a pair of images with a third — generally fainter — counter image, as is the case for the very distant object. The lensed galaxies are particularly numerous, as we are looking in between two mass clumps, in a saddle region where the magnification is quite large.

Abell 2218 was used as a gravitational lens to discover the most distant known object in the universe as of 2004. The object, a galaxy some 13 billion years old, is seen from Earth as it would have been just 750 million years after the Big Bang.
The color of the lensed galaxies is a function of their distances and types. The orange arc is an elliptical galaxy at moderate redshift (z=0.7). The blue arcs are star-forming galaxies at intermediate redshift (z=1–2.5). There is a pair of images in the lower part of the picture of the newly discovered star-forming galaxy at about redshift 7.

[From the image caption:]

This image shows the full overview of the galaxy cluster Abell 2218 and its gravitational lenses. This image was taken by Hubble in 1999 during the Early Release Observations made immediately after the Hubble Servicing Mission 3A. [R67]

Observation:

This cluster's image has so many plasma filaments having structure, it is difficult to find the supposed lens candidates.

Near the bottom and to the left there are 2 segments of a plasma filament which seems to terminate at a bright object (which is a knot, so it's not lensed) at roughly 8 o'clock from the cluster's brightest elliptical galaxy (BCG).

Below this structured segmented filament, there is a broken bright blue thin filament with arc segments at 6 o, 8 o, and 9 o'clock. The blue is not lensed because no galaxies possess that color; their spectrum is predominately synchrotron radiation which results in white from the mix.

At about 2 o'clock from BCG is another elliptical galaxy which is emitting a long orange plasma filament at 4 o'clock, which ends at a knot, so it's not lensed. In exactly the opposite direction from this galaxy, a similar knot was ejected. Opposing jets are not unusual, from the plasmoids at the center of ellipticals.

The top right corner of the image is clipped. In that remaining space, there are 2 ellipticals with vertical plasma filaments having notable structure so they are not lensed.

8.7 Abell 2667

Here is its description:

Abell 2667 is a galaxy cluster. It is one of the most luminous galaxy clusters in the X-ray waveband known at a redshift about 0.2.
This cluster is also a well-known gravitational lens.
On 2 March 2007, a team of astronomers reported the detection of the Comet Galaxy in this cluster. This galaxy is being ripped apart by the cluster's gravitational field and harsh environment. The finding sheds light on the mysterious process by which gas-rich spiral-shaped galaxies might evolve into gas-poor irregular- or elliptical-shaped galaxies over billions of years.

[Caption of image:]

While looking at the galaxy cluster Abell 2667, astronomers found an odd-looking spiral galaxy (shown here in the upper left hand corner of the image) that ploughs through the cluster after being accelerated to at least 3.5 million km/h by the enormous combined gravity of the cluster's dark matter, hot gas and hundreds of galaxies. [R69]

Observation:

That "odd-looking spiral galaxy" is not the most interesting object in this cluster.

On the right-half of the image is a very bright elliptical galaxy, emitting a blue jet in the 10 o'clock direction. To its left is a bright, long, plasma filament, which exhibits both structure and color variation. This complicated filament cannot be a lens illusion.

One might suspect this filament is just an undesirable distraction, to be avoided, by diverting one's attention to the spiral at the opposite corner of the image.

Whatever the high redshift value is of that "ploughing" galaxy, it is certainly not its velocity. The galaxy is not named to enable finding its velocity in NED. Every galaxy redshift is obtained from atoms in the line of sight. There is no galaxy in the universe with a measured 3-dimensional proper velocity. We use only atoms in the line of sight. After many measurements of position over a long time, movement beyond the line of sight, or transverse, could be measured. Without that measurement, there is no justification for "ploughing" in any direction. The outrageous velocity assigned to the galaxy is wrong. Atoms can move fast, but certainly not massive galaxies.

8.8 Abell S1063

Here is its description:

Abell S1063 is a cluster of galaxies located in the constellation Grus.

[Caption of image:]

Abell S1063, a galaxy cluster, was observed by the NASA/ESA Hubble Space Telescope as part of the Frontier Fields programme. The huge mass of the cluster — containing both baryonic matter and dark matter — acts as cosmic magnification glass and deforms objects behind it. In the past astronomers used this gravitational lensing effect to calculate the distribution of dark matter in galaxy clusters. A more accurate and faster way, however, is to study the intracluster light (visible in blue), which follows the distribution of dark matter. [R71]

Observation:

The image is not clear whether the blue haze around the bright giant elliptical galaxy is valid or a false color. The Lyman-alpha emission line is in ultraviolet, so any motion of the proton away from Earth, and toward the galaxy, would redshift its wavelength from UV toward blue.

The high radiant energy from the central galaxy is probably ionizing the surrounding hydrogen atoms which subsequently recombine to emit the Lyman-alpha line.

There are many blue arcs in the image around the central galaxy. These suggest the plasma filaments of protons and electrons are moving tangential, like by the Lorentz force from the galaxy's magnetic field.

8.9 SDSS J103842.59+484918.7 - Cheshire Cat

Excerpt from the Chandra story:

This group of galaxies has been nicknamed the "Cheshire Cat" because of its resemblance to a smiling feline.

Some of the cat-like features are actually distant galaxies whose light has been stretched and bent by the large amounts of mass contained in foreground galaxies.

This is an effect called "gravitational lensing," predicted by Einstein's Theory of General Relativity that is celebrating its 100th anniversary.

X-rays from Chandra show that the two "eye" galaxies and the smaller galaxies associated with them are slamming into one another in a giant galactic collision. [R72]

Observation:

After clicking on the Optical wavelength tab, one can imagine the center of a circle between the 2 bright galaxies. Relative to that center there is an arc from about 2 o'clock to a bright knot at 8 o'clock.
The segments of a circle with changing emission lines to get different colors cannot be from a lens.

The hypothetical lens can only bend the path of light. The color of electromagnetic radiation is driven by the energy distribution in its continuum of wavelengths. To change its color, energy must be exchanged. Gravity alone has no energy to exchange with the passing light. Proposing just gravity can change the energy I light is a violation of thermodynamics. The Doppler Effect uses the kinetic energy in the matter moving which can absorb or emit radiation. The object claimed to be a lens is not participating in any energy transfers with the passing light. It does not absorb or emit anything. All mass outside the light path cannot affect the energy in the light.

The Chandra explanation of the colors in the cat-like features violates thermodynamics and conservation of energy.

With no measurement of the 3-dimensional proper motion of any object, any mention of a collision, of any magnitude, is unjustified conjecture. Measuring only atoms moving in the line of sight is incorrect.

8.10 RCS2 032727-132623

Excerpt from the news release:

A team of astronomers aimed Hubble at one of the most striking examples of gravitational lensing, a nearly 90-degree arc of light in the galaxy cluster RCS2 032727-132623. Hubble's view of the distant background galaxy, which lies nearly 10 billion light-years away, is significantly more detailed than could ever be achieved without the help of the gravitational lens.

Thanks to the presence of a natural "zoom lens" in space, NASA's Hubble Space Telescope got a uniquely close-up look at the brightest "magnified" galaxy yet discovered. This observation provides a unique opportunity to study the physical properties of a galaxy vigorously forming stars when the universe was only one-third its present age.
A so-called gravitational lens is produced when space is warped by a massive foreground object, whether it is the Sun, a black hole, or an entire cluster of galaxies. The light from more-distant background objects is distorted, brightened, and magnified as it passes through this gravitationally disturbed region.
A team of astronomers led by Jane Rigby of NASA's Goddard Space Flight Center in Greenbelt, Md., aimed Hubble at one of the most striking examples of gravitational lensing, a nearly 90-degree arc of light in the galaxy cluster RCS2 032727-132623. Hubble's view of the distant background galaxy is significantly more detailed than could ever be achieved without the help of the gravitational lens.

The distorted image of the galaxy is repeated several times in the foreground lensing cluster, as is typical of gravitational lenses. The challenge for astronomers was to reconstruct what the galaxy really looked like, were it not distorted by the cluster's funhouse-mirror effect.

Hubble's sharp vision allowed astronomers to remove the distortions and reconstruct the galaxy image as it would normally look. The reconstruction revealed regions of star formation glowing like bright Christmas tree bulbs. These are much brighter than any star-formation region in our Milky Way galaxy.

Through spectroscopy, the spreading out of light into its constituent colors, the team plans to analyze these star-forming regions from the inside out to better understand why they are forming so many stars.

Scientists rely on gravitational lenses in order to get a glimpse at the frenetic star-formation regions of distant galaxies in the early universe. Nearby galaxies tend to appear more mature and in the waning stages of star-formation, researchers said.

In the new Hubble image, astronomers aimed the space telescope at the galaxy cluster RCS2 032727-132623, which is surrounded by a nearly 90-degree arc of bright light from an even more distant galaxy. Because of the gravity distortions, the image of the background galaxy is repeated several times — a hallmark feature of gravitational lenses, researchers said.

"The challenge for astronomers was to reconstruct what the galaxy really looked like, were it not distorted by the cluster's funhouse-mirror effect," according to NASA's image description. [R76]

Observation:

There are 4 bright elliptical galaxies roughly together near the center.

the large filament to the left of the center-4 has visible changes in structure along its length, so this filament is plasma, and not a lensed object.

A lensed object should exhibit a consistent arc radius from the lens. These do not. The lens cannot create structure in the illusion.

There are 2 blue plasma filaments above and to the right of the center-4. Both exhibit structure and cannot be lensed objects.

As with other blue filaments in other clusters, they have Lyman-alpha emission regions.

The description implies the astronomers intend to take these individual plasma filaments having Lyman-alpha emission lines, and reconstruct the galaxy's original stars, despite the fact an intact galaxy exhibits the flat continuum of synchrotron radiation. These arcs are not pieces of a picture but are distinct plasma filaments.

Their "funhouse-mirror effect" is just nonsense, suggesting more impossible behaviors for fictitious gravitational lenses.

There are no lensed objects here. There is no galaxy to reconstruct. Everything is as observed; no illusions are needed

8.11 SDSS J0146-0929

From the story and caption:

Hubble Telescope Discovers a Light-Bending 'Einstein Ring' in Space
The graceful arcs at the center of this image from the Hubble Space Telescope are actually the distorted light of distant galaxies, twisted to form an "Einstein ring" by the gravitational influence of the closer galaxy cluster SDSS J0146-0929. (Image credit: ESA/Hubble & NASA; Acknowledgment: Judy Schmidt)

The perfect circle surrounding a galaxy cluster in a new Hubble Space Telescope image is a visual indicator of the huge masses that are bending time and space in that region.
The galaxy cluster, called SDSS J0146-0929, features hundreds of individual galaxies all bound together by gravity. There's so much mass in this region that the cluster is distorting light from objects behind it. This phenomenon is called an Einstein ring.
The ring is created as the light that comes from distant objects, like galaxies, passes by "an extremely large mass, like this galaxy cluster," NASA said in a statement. "In this image, the light from a background galaxy is diverted and distorted around the massive intervening cluster and forced to travel along many different light paths toward Earth, making it seem as though the galaxy is in several places at once."

The ring is named after Albert Einstein, who wrote his theory of general relativity in the early 1900s. In it, he suggested that a massive object would warp space and time. This process is known today as a gravitational lens. When the most massive galaxies and galaxy clusters get in line with a more distant object, they produce an Einstein ring – a type of gravitational lens.

Einstein rings (and gravitational lenses more generally) give astronomers a huge advantage when they are trying to look at faraway objects. The rings and lenses magnify objects that otherwise would be too distant and dim to see in today's telescopes. [R78]

Observation:

The ring appears as 3 individual arcs. Each has its own unique varying structure. The arc at the lower left has a knot, all break the rules established for Hoag's Object. These 3 arcs are luminous plasma filaments and cannot be lensed objects, as claimed.

Astronomers are piling much garbage onto Einstein to justify their delusions.

I cannot find a public archive to confirm their claim of Einstein's declaration of space-time enabling a magnification or multiplication of light sources, in addition to the simple bending of light. Bending was the only goal of Eddington's 1919 expedition. There were never measurements of changes in stellar magnitudes in those experiments prior to 1930.

Einstein had several wrong assumptions in relativity. These are reality:

1) gravity cannot bend light, nor can space-time.
2) Velocity of mass can exceed the velocity of light.

Galaxies and quasars with high redshifts ($z > 1$) from super-luminous protons frequently break his rule or limit.

3) Acceleration from a gravitational field is not equivalent to the acceleration which could result from Newton's force. Unfortunately for Einstein, they are not equivalent. Newton's force affects both bodies, where each mass gets its own acceleration from the mutual force based on its mass, while Einstein's space-time simply ignores an effect on the other body. This mistake renders Einstein an invalid replacement for Newton's force of gravity.

To enforce his first mistake, he needed consequences for someone violating his unjustified first rule, so that rule-breaking observer must have their special, personal time altered to preserve the illusion that Einstein's velocity rule remained intact.

There is no object in the universe subject to only gravitational fields. Every object in the universe, depending on its charge, is subject to the instantaneous combination of the 2 fundamental forces from all the objects around it: gravity and electric, with each diminished by inverse-square of distance between them. Electric force affects only charged objects. Magnetic force affects only charged objects in motion.

When Einstein ignored the special observer's charge and mass and applied only 1 of 3 possible forces on any object, and then used only one narrow context for gravity, he offered a flawed theory.

There is no object in the universe affected by the fictitious warped source and time, in the restricted context of space-time. All are affected by the sum of forces acting on them.

8.12 SPT0615-JD

This is claimed to be a galaxy stretched by a lens, in a story titled NASA's Hubble Spots Embryonic Galaxy SPT0615-JD

This Hubble Space Telescope image shows the farthest galaxy yet seen in an image that has been stretched and amplified by a phenomenon called gravitational lensing. The embryonic galaxy, named SPT0615-JD, existed when the universe was just 500 million years old. Though a few other primitive galaxies have been seen at this early epoch, they have essentially all looked like red dots, given their small size and tremendous distances. However, in this case, the gravitational field of a massive foreground galaxy cluster, called SPT-CL J0615-5746, not only amplified the light from the background galaxy but also smeared the image of it into an arc (about 2 arcseconds long). Image analysis shows that the galaxy weighs in at no more than 3 billion solar masses (roughly 1/100th the mass of our fully grown Milky Way galaxy). It is less than 2,500 light-years across, half the size of the Small Magellanic Cloud, a satellite galaxy of our Milky Way. [R81]

Observation:

Several statements are dubious. First, the light is claimed is claimed to be stretched. Despite the claimed distortion, the galaxy is identified precisely, from type, diameter, and its total mass. I do not have their data but from the image provided, in my opinion it could be classified as an irregular galaxy. I agree with their comment that it looks like either of the Magellanic Clouds.

The description from NASA offers no reason why the distant galaxy is claimed to have its light smeared.

I tried this galaxy's unusual name in the NASA/IPAC Extragalactic Database, but the name was not found.

This story has too many unjustified claims.

9 Arc Mechanism

The arcs noted in section 8 with a variety of galaxy clusters are rather diverse. They are claimed to be an illusion created by a theoretical effect where gravity, rather than the medium, can affect the path of light.

There are 2 distinct types of these arcs:

1) Plasma filament having observed structure. The rule for a lensed object is it has no visible structure. This rule established Hoag's Object as having a real ring, not an illusion looking like a ring.

When an arc has structure, then it cannot be an accepted, lensed object. The explicit rule, set by cosmologists, is being violated.

2) Thin filaments having color but no observed structure.

Explaining the colored fragments requires familiarity of plasma filaments. They usually contain electrons, with ions or protons.

When an ion captures an electron, it emits a characteristic wavelength, when the atom's energy level falls to its ground state. This transfer of internal atomic energy, being held in the electron shells, to radiated energy conforms to thermodynamics.

The Doppler Effect also conforms to thermodynamics, where the kinetic energy of the ion or proton also participates and can be exchanged with the wavelength emission, causing a slight variation in the wavelength depending on the particle's direction. This mix of opposite charges can move long distances without captures within the filament, observed as a gap. Some arcs are observed as fragments while others maintained the motion through the captures, observed as a continuous arc.

Marklund Convection described a mechanism for ions to be collected in a plasma filament. This explains the presence of metallic ions in a plasma filament. As noted earlier, some spiral galaxies (including M31) are known to emit metallic ions. These external rings are observed in distant galaxy clusters which always have spiral galaxies with the giant ellipticals.

10 Microlensing

Microlensing explains the claimed illusion with magnified distant objects. A gravitational lens is invoked for this claimed magnification. Here is its definition.

Gravitational microlensing is an astronomical phenomenon due to the gravitational lens effect. It can be used to detect objects that range from the mass of a planet to the mass of a star, regardless of the light they emit. Typically, astronomers can only detect bright objects that emit much light (stars) or large objects that block background light (clouds of gas and dust). These objects make up only a minor portion of the mass of a galaxy. Microlensing allows the study of objects that emit little or no light. [R84]

Observation:

This behavior of brightening in space is impossible, because it violates the conservation of energy. A magnification is an increase in intensity of the light or an increase in the energy of the propagating wavelengths.

To increase the energy in the wavelengths there must be a defined external source transferring energy to the light. Microlensing never identifies the required external energy source. There is no mechanism for the lens object to somehow transfer any energy to the light passing at a distance.

Therefore, whenever this microlensing is invoked, the observed object must be treated just as observed.

Dr. Dowdye published a paper titled

Important Fundamentals of Mathematical Physics Have Been Found to be Misapplied to Concepts of Gravitational Lensing

Pure classical research in the area of an emission theory predicts there can be absolutely no direct interaction between gravitation and electromagnetism. Convincing astrophysical evidence supports this theory. [R85]

Observation:

If an object is too bright for its distance, then the distance is wrong.

I recently published a book, Cosmology Crisis Cleared, which explains why redshift velocities of all galaxies and quasars are wrong. Any distance based on that velocity is also wrong. [R85]

11 High Redshift Objects

When high redshift objects are observed in distant galaxy clusters. A gravitational lens is invoked to address this conflict.

As noted in my book Cosmology Crisis Cleared, all redshift velocities of galaxies and quasars are measured incorrectly. The spectra of galaxies and quasars are of a different type than stars so the same technique for measuring a redshift cannot be used for all 3 types. [R88]

Galaxies and quasars have a source of synchrotron radiation in their cores. Only a star is a source of thermal radiation, from its photosphere surface.

Atoms can attach to this surface. While attached, the atoms move with the star.

With this combination, shifts of the absorption and emission lines from these atoms can indicate the star's velocity in the line of sight to Earth. Atoms have no surface for attaching with galaxies and quasars, so no atoms can move with them. All absorption and emission lines in their spectra arise from atoms in the line of sight. They indicate nothing about the galaxy or quasar.

This should have been obvious to astronomers. Many galaxies and quasars have redshifts of $z > 1$; all are from the Lyman-alpha emission line when the proton captures an electron forming a hydrogen atom. The z value indicates the proton velocity at the instant of capture. A tiny proton can be accelerated to velocities greater than c. It is probably impossible for either a massive galaxy or quasar to achieve such a velocity. Unfortunately, these impossible, superluminal galaxies and quasars remain unquestioned.

It is very important to recognize the measured velocities of all galaxies and quasars are wrong. Any distance based on velocity, using Hubble's Law, are wrong.

Only distance metrics not using a velocity, or those using standard candles like a Cepheid, remain valid. Since most galaxies do not host a standard candle, most galaxies have a wrong distance.

Until astronomers recognize this mistake, high redshifts are assumed to be a high velocity, as well as a great distance.

When a high redshift object is measured in a galaxy cluster whose galaxies have lower redshifts, this combination is valid.

It is a mistake from confusion to claim a fictitious gravitational lens bent the light from the high redshift object resulting in an illusion of this mix of redshifts in a galaxy cluster.

11.1   Abell 2744 galaxy cluster

Here is a description.

Abell 2744, nicknamed Pandora's Cluster, is a giant galaxy cluster resulting from the simultaneous pile-up of at least four separate, smaller galaxy clusters that took place over a span of 350 million years, and is located approximately 4 billion light years from Earth. The galaxies in the cluster make up less than five percent of its mass. The gas (around 20 percent) is so hot that it shines only in X-rays. Dark matter makes up around 75 percent of the cluster's mass.

This cluster also shows a radio halo along with several other Abell clusters. It has a strong central halo, along with an extended tail, which could either be relic radiation, or an extension of the central halo. [R88]

Observation:

There are many mistakes in this description.

1. The ages, distances and velocities are wrong. All galaxies are measured wrong. Cepheids are not valid at the stated distance, so this is based on a wrong velocity and invalid Hubble's Law.

2. The temperature is wrong. A gas temperature is measured by the kinetic velocity of its particles. A hot gas will be ionized. Ions will be moving by electric and magnetic forces in the cluster. Synchrotron radiation is generated by an electric current whose path is bent by a magnetic field. Synchrotron radiation spans wavelengths from X-ray to radio, depending on the velocity of the electric current which is driven by the strength of an electric field.

3. The ridiculous explanation of the velocity of charged particles is a high temperature. No one claims the velocity of the electric current in the cord to a household appliance is a temperature.

4. The percentage in the story for dark matter is also ridiculous. Dark matter is the excuse when nothing else is available because electromagnetism is ignored. There are galaxies in the cluster. Each is connected by a Birkelund current in a twisted pair as a filament. These intergalactic filaments have been measured by the magnetic field they generate.

5. This galaxy cluster is dominated by electromagnetism, not by the weak force of gravity. Dark matter is the excuse when missing the context in this cluster.

(end of observations)

This cluster is the topic for a story from NASA titled: Galaxy Cluster Abell 2744 from Hubble

This long-exposure Hubble Space Telescope image of the massive galaxy cluster Abell 2744 is the deepest ever made of any cluster of galaxies. The observation shows some of the faintest and youngest galaxies ever detected in space.

Abell 2744, located in the constellation Sculptor, appears in the foreground of this image. It contains several hundred galaxies as they looked 3.5 billion years ago. The immense gravity in Abell 2744 acts as a gravitational lens to warp space and brighten and magnify images of nearly 3,000 distant background galaxies.

The more distant galaxies appear as they did more than 12 billion years ago, not long after the big bang. This image is part of an unprecedented long-distance view of the universe from an ambitious collaborative project among the NASA Great Observatories called The Frontier Fields. Over several years, the project observed select patches of the sky for the purpose of better understanding galaxy evolution. [R90]

Observation:

As noted many times previously, all ages and distances have no justification. Hubble's Law is invalid as well as all velocities.

Claims that gravity can "brighten and magnify images" are wrong. Gravity cannot transmit energy into light passing by at a distance.

This conjectured use of gravity cannot justify the violation of the conservation of energy.

All the distant galaxies are truly as observed. Apparently, the astronomers cannot accept their faint luminosity at their calculated distance from Hubble's Law.

Invoking gravitational lensing is the wrong solution to the wrong application of the invalid Hubble's Law.

11.2 Frontier Fields Project

Its home page article is titled:

A sea of Galaxies in the Final Frontier Fields Views

The final observations of the Frontier Fields project are now in the books, although the hard work of analyzing the data has just begun. Views of the stunningly beautiful galaxy cluster Abell 370 and its parallel field mark the end of this ambitious observing campaign, which began in October 2013.

The photogenic Abell 370 contains an astounding assortment of several hundred galaxies tied together by the mutual pull of gravity. Located approximately 4 billion light-years away in the constellation Cetus, the Sea Monster, this immense cluster is a rich mix of a variety of galaxy shapes. [R91]

Observation:

Abell 370 was described in section Galaxies with External Arcs.

However, this article provides an illustration of the theoretical gravitational lens mechanism. Here it is.

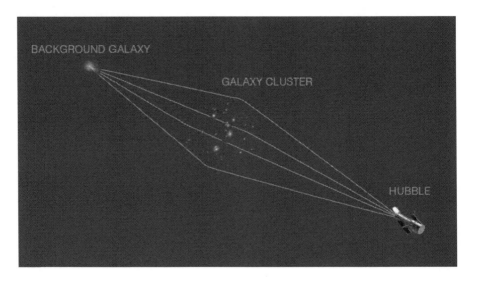

Its caption:

Gravitational lensing magnifies background galaxies that are otherwise presently unobservable.

Observation:

There are many requirements to achieve magnification, which are only conjectures.

First, gravity must bend light regardless of distance from the lens object (but it doesn't). Second, all intervening galaxies must bend the light path at exactly the correct and different angle for all galaxies in a random distribution within the cluster. Third, all angles must converge at exactly the Hubble Telescope in near-Earth orbit.

If all galaxies do not exactly match with their contribution, then the images at Hubble would be: a) blurred?, b) dimmer?, or c) Hubble will get images scattered around this cluster when not viewing directly at the center of the cluster, where the light past each galaxy does not converge with the others.

If there are observations of a tiny light at random locations in the dark night sky due to case (c), those reports are not making the news

This is not astrophysics. This is incredible nonsense.

Magnification is not possible because it requires adding energy to light in passing; this violates the conservation of energy.

11.3 Searching for lenses - CLASS

CLASS is Cosmic Lens All-Sky Survey.

The Cosmic Lens All-Sky Survey (CLASS), is an international (USA, UK and Netherlands) collaborative project to map more than 10,000 radio sources in order to create the largest and best studied statistical sample of radio-loud gravitationally lensed systems. With this survey, combined with detailed studies of the lenses found therein, powerful constraints can be placed on the cosmography (ie. expansion rate, mean density, and cosmological constant) of the Universe. CLASS is aimed at identifying lenses where multiple images are formed from compact flat-spectrum radio sources. The lens configurations should be easily identifiable in the radio maps. Thus, CLASS is most efficient at finding galaxy-mass lenses (which will dominate the counts for surveys not targeted at clusters) with separations of around a few arcseconds.

One of the most important uses of galaxy-mass lenses is in the determination of cosmological parameters. In particular, time delays measured between the components in multiple image systems can directly determine the angular-diameter distances to the lens and lensed objects, and therefore the Hubble constant H_0. Because the lensing equations depend on a ratio of distances, they are not as sensitive to the deceleration parameter q_0 and cosmological constant, although if accurate delays were found to a number of lenses at a range of redshifts, some measurement of these quantities could be made. Of course, the success of the method depends upon the presence of measurable variability in the lensed source, and the ability to construct a well-constrained mass model for the lens, and thus only a few lenses found in CLASS will be ``golden lenses" suitable as cosmological standards. The CLASS group is monitoring the quadruple lens 1608+656 found in the first year of the survey. In addition to specific lenses, the survey statistics as a whole can provide constraints on cosmological models. A search for gravitational lenses in the northern hemisphere (Cosmic Lens All Sky Survey, CLASS), done in radio frequencies using the Very Large Array (VLA) in New Mexico, led to the discovery of 22 new lensing systems, a major milestone. This has opened a whole new avenue for research ranging from finding very distant objects to finding values for cosmological parameters so we can understand the universe better. [R95]

Observation:

The critical aspect of this survey is **redshift**. Astronomers believe this measurement can be used to detect distant objects. Unfortunately, they are always measured wrong. Every high redshift object, both galaxy and quasar, are always a redshift of the Lyman-alpha emission line, which is emitted when a proton captues an electron. When a proton is moving faster tha c in the line of sight, it is unjustified to believe that whatever is behind this tiny proton is also moving faster than c. With this confusion, this study cannot help us "understand the universe better."

There is a similar survey planned for the southern hemisphere.

Here is a description.

A similar search in the southern hemisphere would be a very good step towards complementing the northern hemisphere search as well as obtaining other objectives for study. If such a search is done using well-calibrated and well-parameterized instrument and data, a result similar to the northern survey can be expected. The use of the Australia Telescope 20 GHz (AT20G) Survey data collected using the Australia Telescope Compact Array (ATCA) stands to be such a collection of data. Full detail of the project is currently under works for publication. [R96]

Observation:

Nothing more can be reviewed until they publish.

11.4 first discovery by CLASS

They published a paper titled:

CLASS B1152+199 and B1359+154: Two New Gravitational Lens Systems Discovered in the Cosmic Lens All-Sky Survey

[T]wo new candidate lensed systems were discovered: CLASS B1152+199 and B1359+154. B1152+199 is a 1.6" double, with a background quasar at z=1.019 lensed by a foreground galaxy at z=0.439. [R96]

Observation:

They measured a quasar with a redshift of z=1.019 near a galaxy with a redshift of 0.439.

Because cosmology is confused by redshifts, the assumption is the high redshift must be far behind the low redshift.

This is wrong, as demonstrated in this combination. The unnamed galaxy probably has its redshift from neutral hydrogen atoms in the line of sight. They cannot indicate the velocity of a galaxy behind them.

Every galaxy and quasar with z > 1 is always a redshifted Lyman-alpha line which is emitted by a superluminal proton capturing an electron. Tiny protons can be superluminal but is ridiculous to believe galaxies and quasars can be.

In this CLASS pair of low redshift galaxy and superluminal quasar, the ridiculous explanation is the quasar is lensed. This means the high redshift quasar is just an illusion when observed next to the low redshift galaxy.

There is no illusion; there is no gravitational lens.

The quasar is where it is observed.

From their first discovery, CLASS is declaring a lens wherever the high redshift object is near a low redshift object. In reality, this can happen. Halton Arp observed many of these combinations, and reported some of them in his book Seeing Red. At the time, other scientists dismissed his reports.

CLASS is reporting the same combination Halton Arp reported many years ago.

11.5 Quadripple quasar found by CLASS

Another paper from CLASS is titled:

A Quadruple-Lens System Found in the CLASS Gravitational Lens Survey

We report here the first discovery of a gravitational lens from the survey: 1608+656, a quadruply imaged object with a maximum separation of 2."1 . Images from the Palomar 5 m and Keck 10 m telescopes show the lensed images and the lensing galaxy. An optical spectrum obtained with the Palomar 5 m telescope indicates a redshift of z=0.6304 for the lensing galaxy. No conclusive redshift for the lensed object has been determined, although a single strong emission line is found at 9240 A in the Keck low-resolution imaging spectrograph spectrum. The two most likely identifications for this line are H beta (z=0.90) and Mg II (z=2.30). [R98]

Observation:

CLASS is reporting the combination reported by Halton Arp, with a Seyfert galaxy ejecting a pair of quasars, but in the case reported less often, the Seyfert ejects 2 pairs, in opposing directions, with result of each separated by 90 degrees from the next.

The galaxy here is confirmed as a Seyfert by the Magnesium ion emission line. Seyfert galaxies are in the LINER type, because of their metallic ion emission lines when observing its spectrum only in their core.

When the Seyfert ejects the quasar, it passes some of those metallic ions to the quasar. Every quasar is characterized by its many metallic ion emission lines.

High redshift quasars also have the high redshift from the Lyman-alpha line emitted by a superluminal proton capturing an electron.

There is no gravitational lens here.

There is no illusion here at 1608+656, because the Seyfert ejected 4 quasars which remain nearby.

12 Particle Rings

There are many known rings of particles in our solar system.

Given that everybody, having any size, in the solar system is in the stream of charged particles from the Sun, known as the solar wind, all bodies can attain an electric charge. The solar wind contains some electrons, while the rest are protons or atomic nuclei.

The Sun has a measured positive charge, so it sheds particles with most having a positive charge.

All the gas giants have magnetic fields. Moving charged particles are subject to the Tangential Lorentz force from a magnetic field.

Among the planets having known particle rings are Jupiter (4 rings), Saturn (7), Uranus (2), Neptune (5).

Among the asteroids having particle rings is Chariklo (2).

These rings are probably sustained by a mix of the force of gravity and electrostatic forces between particles which could be charged and the primary body.

None of these rings are illusions from a gravitational lens.

13 Black Hole

A black hole is an object which is claimed to have a force of gravity too strong, or space-time curvature too steep, for light to escape.

Here is its basic description.

A black hole is a region of spacetime where gravity is so strong that nothing — no particles or even electromagnetic radiation such as light — can escape from it. The theory of general relativity predicts that a sufficiently compact mass can deform spacetime to form a black hole. The boundary of no escape is called the event horizon. Although it has an enormous effect on the fate and circumstances of an object crossing it, according to general relativity it has no locally detectable features. [R100]

Observation:

No amount of gravity can stop light. Gravity cannot even bend light.

Black holes are always placed at an X-ray source, like at the center of a galaxy. This is why black holes are so important in cosmology. Otherwise X-ray point sources could not be explained. By claiming the black hole is invisible, then it explains radiation for a source other than mass, which is the synchrotron mechanism of an electric current with a separate magnrtic field to bend the path of the current.

Cosmologists fail to recognize sources of synchrotron radiation, which can span from X-ray to radio wavelengths.

This black hole topic was covered earlier in this book. Wal Thornhill provided a good explanation of a plasmoid in a YouTube video: Thornhill: Black Hole or Plasmoid? [R50]

A plasmoid is in the core of an elliptical galaxy, like M87.

13.1 Black hole and space-time in graphics

Graphical representations of space-time curvature are an intentional deception.

This unedited image from NASA will help explain this deception. [R101]

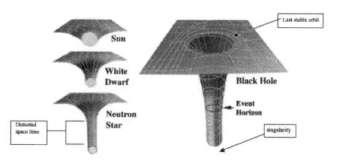

In relativity, when the observer is moving near an object with a gravitational field their current motion is obtained in 4 parameters having the observer's change in 3-D space, and the change in time during each incremental motion. These values are manipulated to curve the path toward the source of the gravitational field.
This curvature affects only the path of the moving observer, so no one else is affected.

The left column in the image illustrates how the special observer's path in space-time could be curved when they are passing by the Sun, a white dwarf, or a neutron star.

For all other observers, the Sun, the white dwarf, or the neutron star, are observed using classical physics, such as electromagnetic radiation.

The image is deceptive because there is no distinction between a) the special, moving observer (who is moving to or near these objects) and b) all other observers (who observe no curvature).

One could present an edited image to represent the view for all other observers by simply removing those curved graphics which show the observer's distorted path in space-time. At the lower left is the legend "distorted space time." This explicitly notes the specific context for this image. That edited image removes the deception by showing the real universe, in which all observers can observe and measure objects. Astronomers are in this set of observers excluding the special observer. Astronomers nearly always use the celestial coordinate system, but rarely the Cartesian coordinate system which is the basis of space-time. Therefore, astronomers are not affected by the special observer's motion past a particular body in physical space.

The right column in the image has the most blatant deception. Here is the black hole.

The single arrow pointing to "Singularity" (at bottom right) actually points to 2 entities.

1) The physical mass at that location in physical space,

The mass is not shown in this column, though each mass was shown in the left column.

2) A point in the observer's reference frame or coordinate system.

The point is not in the image simply because a point has no size.

In basic terms of geometry, the center of an object, regardless of its shape, is described as a point.
In the mathematical exercise of space-time curvature for an extreme mass, the path of the observer must terminate at the center of the mass, or a point. This point in geometry is called the singularity in physics.

This singularity is called a black hole though technically it is a black point. There is no hole in anything; it is just a point in the special observer's reference frame.

The image could be edited as suggested to remove the graphs from the respective columns; then the mass should be shown here, consistent with the others, to help fix the deception for all observers other than the one moving (i.,e., non-inertial).
The deceptive graphic hides this mistake in physics with two simultaneous conflicting entities where one entity is a concept, just a point in a coordinate system, while the other entity is a physical mass.

For all other observers, the mass remains and can be observed and measured and, as a mass, it is still subject to the force of gravity from other bodies. It is a violation of physics to claim this mass simply disappears to all other observers.

It is also a violation of physics to claim the mass remains intact, still generating its gravitational field, while compressed within a geometric point, or the claimed singularity.

Physicists chose to combine these two conflicting entities from geometry and physics, resulting in something physically impossible.

There should be another arrow in the image next to that of Singularity and pointing to the same point but with the legend "Impossible"

There is no such thing as a black hole. This will be explained further in its section.

Probably, if graphical representations of space-time curvature were not deceptive then impossible entities like black holes would go away.

To present the correct consequences of a proposed black hole, the image for all observers, except for the special observer, who have no distorted space-time, the bottom right should have this note inserted using the Sun's graphic icon (instead of O):

(Begin note)

Milky Way SMBH has O x 4.1 million visible to all other observers.

(End of note)

That simple change to the figure clearly unveils the deception because there is NO real mass of that size, being observed by astronomers when they are viewing that specific location claimed for that super massive black hole.

Black holes fail just by remembering the rules of relativity.

Space-time curvature is the path of the special observer. It is not an attribute of the space that they could or did move through.

13.2 Event horizon

An event horizon was mentioned in the basic description of a black hole at the start of this section.

Here is a definition and description.

In astrophysics, an event horizon is a boundary beyond which events cannot affect an observer.

Stephen Hawking, who was one of the leading developers of theories to describe black holes, eventually concluded that "the absence of event horizons means that there are no black holes – in the sense of regimes from which light can't escape to infinity." [R106]

Observation:

There is no justification for claiming the force of gravity can decrease to zero the velocity of light, which is not a body having mass (which could be affected by gravity). Gravity cannot affect an electric field or a magnetic field. These fields are the mechanism of electromagnetic radiation, or light.

Black holes do not exist.
Stephen Crothers has written numerous papers and presented at numerous conferences on the subject of black holes. [R106]

He (and others) reached the same conclusion long ago.

14 Final Conclusion

There are several distant celestial objects having accepted real rings. Both Hoag's Object and the Cartwheel Galaxy are known to many astronomers.

Galaxies with ring or arc features are too distant for space probes.

Rings and arcs around very distant galaxies are always dismissed as only an illusion. Plasma behaviors are never considered.

These claims of an illusion can be dismissed by providing a reasonable explanation for each observation.

I offered my tentative explanation for an arc around a distant galaxy using several examples. Some claimed lensed objects are clearly plasma filaments having definite structure so claiming those are lensed objects is just a mistake. With others, the arc is a plasma filament with an ion or proton capturing an electron to emit the atom's characteristic wavelength. When these captures are periodic within the travel of particles within the filament, then it can be seen as arcs rather than as a continuous arc. Alternately, the plasma moving in the filament alternates between arc mode and dark mode based on the current excitation of that segment of the filament,
It is impossible for a direct confirmation of the specific mechanism without direct spectrum measurements of every component, or by a closer observation of an arc.

I expect Hannes Alfven or other plasma physicists have duplicated and explained each and every arc or ring observation noted in this book.

My goal was to show a gravitational lens is not a viable explanation for them.

The arcs and rings are certainly **not** an illusion from a gravitational lens.

These claimed illusions, with the excuse of a hypothetical gravitational lens, are just avoiding proper physics, and its progression to include plasma physics (which arose so long ago, in 1970).

All arcs and rings in distant galaxy clusters can be explained by applying known behaviors in plasma physics.

There is no evidence for the theoretical gravitational lens behavior. Gravity cannot bend the path of light. Per James Clerk Maxwell, only the medium at the instant can affect the propagation velocity of the synchronized, perpendicular electric and magnetic fields which is the combination serving as the mechanism for carrying the energy within electromagnetic radiation. The book described the few mechanisms for bending the path of light, but each is dependent on the medium. They include a prism, and refraction either by atmospheric density changes, or by the solar corona (which is plasma in an electric field).

I self-published several books about cosmology. [R108]

The science of cosmology remains broken for 3 significant reasons:

1. Measured redshifts are mistakes rendering the universe impossible to explain with so many wrong theories based on bad data. Nonsense like universe expansion, dark energy, and a big bang must be removed.

2. Plasma physics must be integrated into cosmology. Nonsense like black holes, dark matter, and gravitational lensing must be removed.

3. The Robitaille LMH model for stars must replace the 100+ year old fusion model.

   Stars do not consume themselves by fusion.

   Non-existent black holes do not have a destiny of consuming everything else.

   Galaxies and their stars are electrical, connected to their environment. None are isolated. The term island universe for a galaxy denied its correct electrical context.

   There was no mythical creation event called a big bang.

   Depending on whether each entity has an electrical charge, everything is subject to the simultaneous and instantaneous forces of gravity and electromagnetism, but these are diminished by inverse-square of distance.

15 References

The references in the book are available as clickable links from a page in the author's web site.

1. Start web browser

2. Go to this site: www.cosmologyview.com

3. Make sure the browser is on the correct home page:

Cosmology Views

4. Scroll to near the middle.

5. Select: **Books by the author**

This page presents information for each pdf or book of mine.

Locate the columns for this pdf or book.

6. Locate

Gravitational Lens Illusions

7. Below it, locate the date of this book's edition:

12/06/2021 References

8. Select: **References** after the correct date.

The selected page will list the references in the book by page number, with a link to that reference.

Each link indicates whether it is to a pdf, a YouTube video, or a URL link to a web page. The user is aware of what the browser will do with the link.

Made in the USA
Columbia, SC
20 December 2021

51595775R00061